THE POEMS in this book are available in full on two cassettes, JUR 00A6 and JUR 00A7, issued by Audio-Visual Productions, 15 Temple Sheen Road, London, SW14 7PY. They are read by Angela Baddeley, Richard Attenborough, Hugh Dixon, Peter O'Shaughnessy, V. C. Clinton-Baddeley, Anne Cross (aged 8) and the following poets, who read their own work: Kingsley Amis, Thomas Blackburn, Charles Causley, D. J. Enright, Zulfikar Ghose, John Heath-Stubbs, Ted Hughes, Bernard Kops, C. Day Lewis, Michell Raper, Vernon Scannell, Stevie Smith, Anthony Thwaite and John Wain.

Here Today

Introduced by
TED HUGHES

Hutchinson

London Melbourne Sydney Auckland Johannesburg

Hutchinson & Co. (Publishers) Ltd

An imprint of the Hutchinson Publishing Group

17-21 Conway Street, London W1P 6JD

Hutchinson Publishing Group (Australia) Pty Ltd
PO Box 496, 16-22 Church Street, Hawthorne, Melbourne, Victoria 3122

Hutchinson Group (NZ) Ltd
32-34 View Road, PO Box 40-086, Glenfield, Auckland 10

Hutchinson Group (SA) (Pty) Ltd
PO Box 337, Bergvlei 2012, South Africa

First published 1963
Reprinted 1964 (twice), 1965 (twice), 1966, 1967, 1969,
1971, 1975, 1976, 1978, 1980, 1981, 1983, 1984

Cover design by
JOHN SEARES RILEY

Printed and bound in Great Britain by
Anchor Brendon Ltd, Tiptree, Essex

ISBN 0 09 068171 1

Acknowledgements

For permission to reprint copyright material the publishers are indebted to the following: the authors and Faber and Faber Ltd for *The Secret Sharer* from *Fighting Terms* by Thom Gunn, *View of a Pig* from *Lupercal* by Ted Hughes, *Rising Five* from *The Pot Geranium* by Norman Nicholson, and *Conquerors* from *The Haunted Garden* by Henry Treece; the authors and Routledge and Kegan Paul Ltd for *The Housewife* from *Voyage from Spring* by Michael Baldwin and *The 'Black' Country* from *The Laughing Hyena* by D. J. Enright; the authors and Putnam and Co. Ltd for *The Citizens* from *The Next Word* by Thomas Blackburn and *Autobiographical Note* from *A Sense of Danger* by Vernon Scannell; the authors and *The Listener* for *A Moment of Respect* by Edwin Brock (to be published in *With Love from Judas*, Scorpion Press) and *Disturbances* by Anthony Thwaite; the authors and Rupert Hart Davis Ltd for *Timothy Winters*, *Nursery Rhyme of Innocence and Experience* and *My Friend Maloney* from *Union Street* and *Johnny Alleluia* by Charles Causley, *Cynddylan on a Tractor* and *Abersoch* from *Song at the Year's Turning* and *Poetry for Supper* by R. S. Thomas; the author and Rupert Hart Davis Ltd and David Higham Associates for *At Any Rate* and *Dooley is a Traitor* from *Possible Laughter* by James Michie; the author and André Deutsch Ltd for *In Memory of Jane Fraser* from *For the Unfallen* by Geoffrey Hill; the author, André Deutsch Ltd and John Johnson for *In Midwinter a Wood was . . .* and *The Fox-Coloured Pheasant Enjoyed his Peace* from *Water, Rock and Sand* by Peter Levi; the authors and Penguin Books for *Peach, Plum or Apricot* from

The Dream of Peter Mann by Bernard Kops and *Your Attention Please* by Peter Porter from *Penguin Modern Poets, Volume 2*; the author and Victor Gollancz Ltd for *Autobiographical Fragment* from *A Case of Samples* by Kingsley Amis; the author and Longmans, Green and Co. Ltd for *Death on a Live Wire* from *Death on a Live Wire* by Michael Baldwin; the author and Oxford University Press for *Elegy for William Hubbard* from *With Love Somehow* by Tony Connor; the author, Methuen and Co. Ltd and David Higham Associates for *A History of the Flood* from *A Charm against the Toothache* by John Heath-Stubbs; the author and The Cresset Press for *And Because* from *Straight Lines and Unicorns* by John Knight; the author and Jonathan Cape Ltd for *Sheepdog Trials in Hyde Park* from *The Gate* by C. Day Lewis; the author and Chapman and Hall Ltd for *Harold's Leap* from *Harold's Leap* by Stevie Smith; the author and Macmillan and Co. Ltd for *Au Jardin des Plantes* from *Weep Before God* by John Wain; John Arden for *The Lobster Pot*; John Arden and *Twentieth Century* for *Johnny Finn*; Michael Baldwin for *Social Study*; William Dunlop for *Landscape as Werewolf* and William Dunlop and *Granta* for *Cat*; Raymond Garlick for *Tenby*; Zulfikar Ghose for *Coming to England*; Gordon Gridley for *The Hero*; B. S. Johnson for *Song of the Wagondriver*; Richard Kell for *Pigeons*; George MacBeth for *The Drawer*; Jack Marriott for *Street Scene*; Adrian Mitchell for *A Child is Singing*; Julian Mitchell for *Holiday* and Julian Mitchell and *Poetry* for *Lament for the Cowboy Life*; Michell Raper for *Morning Glory* and *Sunday Morning in the North*; Vernon Scannell for *First Fight*; Alan Sillitoe for *Car Fights Cat*; Robin Skelton for *The Day Larry was Stretched*; Hal Summers for *Robin*; Rex Taylor and *Tomorrow* for *The Poster*; Anthony Thwaite for *Hedgehog*; Richard Weber and *Satis* for *The Hunt*; H. Webster for *Street Gang*; Bernard Kops for *Skyman*; and the author and William Heinemann Ltd for *Leaving Town* from *Collected Poems* by James Reeves. *I Remember, I Remember* by Philip Larkin is reprinted from *The Less Deceived* by permission of the Marvell Press.

Contents

CREATURES

TWO STORIES

SCENES

POINTS OF VIEW

Introduction

LISTENING TO POETRY

A poet is excited about the poem he is writing. He is so full of this thing he is writing about he can't take time to set it all down tediously with every detail, as if he were making a police report. Even though he composes slowly, he has his mind on nothing but the essentials. If he were demolishing a building in the same spirit in which he writes his poem he would not unpick it brick by brick, as a novelist would, but plant high explosive at each corner and bring the whole lot down in four bangs, or preferably in one fourfold bang. Poetry, at its simplest, is something like that. On page 35 is a poem called *Social Study* by Michael Baldwin. If you were to write that out as a prose story, giving all the details, it would be a long piece of writing and hardly one person in ten would want to read it. As a poem it takes only twenty lines, and everybody will want to read it. Nine readers out of ten will read it again. That is because in the poem the story is compressed into a few verses, so each verse jumps into the reader's mind opening like an explosion, excitingly. The poem is saying many things in a few words, and that sets our imagination working. When a writer tries to tell every single detail, as some prose-writers do in their stories, our imagination just goes dead, it gets bored. This art of explosive compression is one of the first virtues of poetry.

What is a poet's excitement? Something has so excited him that he is mentally dancing and singing. He can be excited to sadness, as well as to joyfulness, and quietly as well as violently. He can be excited to countless varied feelings. And his inner singing and dancing fit the feelings. But because he is a poet, and full of words, his song-dance does not break into real song, as it would if he were a musician, or into real dancing, as it would if he were a dancer. It breaks into words. And the dance and the song come out somehow within the words. The dance makes the words move in a pattern, which we call metre and versification. The song makes the sound of the lines rise and fall against each other, which we call the music of poetry, or the cadence. It sounds complicated, but it happens inevitably when people set to writing poetry. This art of dance in words and music in words are two more of the principal virtues of poetry.

So three things are blended in a poem. A story, or it may be a description, or it may be a man telling his thoughts. A dance. And a song. And so, besides being told a string of facts, we are made to dance them out inwardly, and sing out the feelings behind them inwardly. As a result, the facts go more deeply into our minds and affect us more strongly than if they were just counted off to us in prose. And the dance and the song leave us strangely refreshed, as dancing and singing do leave us refreshed.

Now we see why poetry should be read aloud. The string of facts in a poem are probably the least important thing about it, though they are important. What matters most, since we are listening to poetry and not to prose, is that we hear the dance and the song in the words. The dance and the song engage the deepest roots of our minds, and carry the poet's words down into our depths. This is the way a poem that seems plain-spoken and downright, such as *Au Jardin des Plantes* by John Wain, on page 124, still leaves us with a sense of having been listening to some odd sort of music. And the final sway over our minds that the poem has is largely the sway of the hidden waves of song, and the motion of the dance in the phrasing of the words, that it compels us to share as we read or hear it.

When we have begun to listen for these things, and to find pleasure in hearing them, we have begun to understand poetry. And we begin to be glad the poet did not speak his mind in prose.

TED HUGHES

PORTRAITS

Timothy Winters

Timothy Winters comes to school
With eyes as wide as a football-pool,
Ears like bombs and teeth like splinters:
A blitz of a boy is Timothy Winters.

His belly is white, his neck is dark,
And his hair is an exclamation-mark.
His clothes are enough to scare a crow
And through his britches the blue winds blow.

When teacher talks he won't hear a word
And he shoots down dead the arithmetic-bird,
He licks the patterns off his plate
And he's not even heard of the Welfare State.

Timothy Winters has bloody feet
And he lives in a house on Suez Street,
He sleeps in a sack on the kitchen floor
And they say there aren't boys like him any more.

Old Man Winters likes his beer
And his missus ran off with a bombardier,
Grandma sits in the grate with a gin
And Timothy's dosed with an aspirin.

The Welfare Worker lies awake
But the law's as tricky as a ten-foot snake,
So Timothy Winters drinks his cup
And slowly goes on growing up.

[over

At Morning Prayers the Master helves
For children less fortunate than ourselves,
And the loudest response in the room is when
Timothy Winters roars 'Amen!'

So come one angel, come on ten:
Timothy Winters says 'Amen
Amen amen amen amen.'
Timothy Winters, Lord.

Amen.

Charles Causley

Morning Glory

My father would begin each day
By standing in the backyard door
And giving one tremendous sneeze,
Mid-way between a gasp and roar:

Would clap a fist before his eyes,
And give a kind of stamping dance,
As if his spirit wept and sang
To hear such goodly resonance.

And even now I can remember
His gaiters, and the scads of mire
He kicked before him, as this greeting
Sprang from his nostrils like a fire.

And cocks in every neighbouring yard
Would lift their heads, and strut and stir,
Sensing the challenge of some odd,
Irate and twanging chanticlere.

Michell Raper

Cynddylan on a Tractor

Ah, you should see Cynddylan on a tractor.
Gone the old look that yoked him to the soil;
He's a new man now, part of the machine,
His nerves of metal and his blood oil.
The clutch curses, but the gears obey
His least bidding, and lo, he's away
Out of the farmyard, scattering hens.
Riding to work now as a great man should,
He is the knight at arms breaking the fields'
Mirror of silence, emptying the wood
Of foxes and squirrels and bright jays.
The sun comes over the tall trees
Kindling all the hedges, but not for him
Who runs his engine on a different fuel.
And all the birds are singing, bills wide in vain,
As Cynddylan passes proudly up the lane.

R. S. Thomas

Song of the Wagondriver

My first love was the ten-ton truck
They gave me when I started,
And though she played the bitch with me
I grieved when we were parted.

Since then I've had a dozen more,
The wound was quick to heal,
And now it's easier to say
I'm married to my wheel.

I've trunked it north, I've trunked it south,
On wagons good and bad,
But none was ever really like
The first I ever had.

The life is hard, the hours are long,
Sometimes I cease to feel,
But I go on, for it seems to me
I'm married to my wheel.

Often I think of my home and kids,
Out on the road at night,
And think of taking a local job
Provided the money's right.

Two nights a week I see my wife,
And eat a decent meal,
But otherwise, for all my life,
I'm married to my wheel.

B. S. Johnson

The Hero

Young Jimmy Stone lived a life of his own,
but he shared a small room with his brother.
He woke up at six from a kick in the head,
the alarm-clock bawling beside his bed;
he envied his kid-brother, Ken, sleeping sound,
but he had to get up for his paper-round.
His hand wouldn't grip; he closed one fist;
kneading his eyes to clear the mist,
he fought off sleep with a yawn and a groan,
then he knocked out the clock with the other.

The house was still, the air was chill,
and his teeth began to chatter.
He sized himself up in the long wardrobe glass
and decided his chest and his biceps would pass,
pulled a black woollen windcheater over his head,
rummaged round for his socks at the foot of the bed,
half-considered a wash, but decided the strain
wasn't worth it, he'd get a good rinse in the rain,
so he guzzled his thermos-flask off at a swill,
and was off down the road at a clatter.

To cover the mile from his house to the shop,
Jimmy stretched his imagination.
On the six-minute run he'd scored many a goal
as left-winger for Spurs, but this morning his role
was cast as a gun-slinging, wild desperado
who cantered alone through the streets of Laredo.

Beneath him his stallion, a powerful roan,
rang echoing rhythms of steel upon stone;
Jimmy felt for his gun-butt and reined to a stop
in the courtyard in front of the station.

It wasn't the bank he was going to crack,
nor the Wells-Fargo strongroom to plunder;
he'd robbed plenty before, and he'd rob 'em again,
but he knew they'd unloaded just then from the
    train
some freight much more precious than gold, a
    great stack
of papers that carried death-warrants in black
banner headlines: 'The Stone Brothers break out of
    jail!
One wounded—gone East—full descriptions.' The
    tale
mustn't break till a doctor had dressed Kenny's back,
then they'd ride for the border like thunder.
Kicking open the door, he strode into the store;
the news-sheets were stacked on the counter.
The storekeeper hardly looked up from the scales,
unpacking tobacco from seven-pound bales
into dark, lacquered jars, and checking the weight;
not another soul near, by a good stroke of fate.
Leaning over the counter, Jim pitched a half-dollar
to roll past the storekeeper's feet; with a holler
the old guy was grubbing about on the floor.
Counterfeit beat the draw, this encounter.

[over

Jimmy grabbed all the papers up under one arm,
while the storekeeper grovelled and grumbled,
then ran out to his horse, waiting, patient, on guard,
in the rain-washed, deserted, dawn-desolate yard,
swung up in the saddle and gave a quick chuck
to the rein, heading home, laughing out at his luck.
When a doctor had strapped Kenny's back good and
    tight
and he'd rested a while, they would hit out at night;
no time could be lost, for he knew an alarm
would be raised when his trick had been rumbled.

Unpursued and alone, he steadied the roan
to a canter, checked chamber and trigger.
In the thud of his newly shod boots on the stone
and the turf of the verge, he could feel through the
    bone
the power of the steel-sinewed stallion's stride.
'Steady, Smoky,' he murmured, 'we'll easy outride
any posse——' he woke startled-stiff as a van
pulled up sharp at his side and his governor, a man
whose one driving ambition was simply to own
twenty thousand, leaned out with a snigger.

'Who you talking to, Jimmy? You'd better take
    care—
people might think you're getting half-witted.
Here, give us your papers—you took the wrong
    stack—
and snap out of your dreaming! Next time, it's the
    sack!'

Jimmy stared at the shop-keeper's bumptious
    behind,
despising his shop-shape, cash-register mind.
A man whose one dream is of winning the pools
thinks those who make stories are liars or fools;
the sharp schemer and dreamer have nothing to
    share,
and each by the other is pitied.

Gordon Gridley

My Friend Maloney

My friend Maloney, eighteen
  Swears like a sentry
Got into trouble two years back
  With the local gentry.

Parson and squire's sons
  Informed a copper.
The magistrate took one look at Maloney.
  Fixed him proper.

Talked of the crime of youth
  The innocent victim.
Maloney never said a blind word
  To contradict him.

Maloney of Gun Street
  Back of the Nuclear Mission,
Son of the town whore,
  Blamed television.

Justice, as usual, triumphed.
  Everyone felt fine.
Things went deader.
  Maloney went up the line.

Maloney learned one lesson:
  Never play the fool
With the products of especially a minor
  public school.

Maloney lost a thing or two
  At that institution.
First shirt, second innocence
  The old irresolution.

Found himself a girl-friend
  Sharp suit, sharp collars.
Maloney on a moped
  Pants full of dollars.

College boys on the corner
  In striped, strait blazers
Look at old Maloney
  Eyes like razors.

You don't need talent, says Maloney.
  You don't need looks.
All I got you got, fellers.
  You can keep your thick books.

Parson got religion
  Squire, in the end, the same,
The magistrate went over the wall.
  Life, said Maloney, 's a game.

Consider then the case of Maloney
  College boys, parson, squire, beak.
Who was the victor and who was the victim?
  Speak.

Charles Causley

Johnny Finn
(*A Nursery Rhyme*)

Johnny Finn rode out one day
In his four-wheel car along the broad highway.
He saw a snowdrop white and gay:
  I want the snowdrop.
  Then he threw it away.

Johnny Finn crawled on the floor
Between the table and the door.
He saw his mother's cloak of grey.
  I want the cloak.
  Then he threw it away.

Johnny Finn lay in his bed
With yellow blankets round his head.
He saw a black cat come in to play.
  I want the cat.
  Then he threw it away.

Johnny Finn lived a life of pleasure,
His hands reached out four ways for treasure.
Silver and gold by night and day.
  I want all the long life:
  To throw it away.

John Arden

The Housewife

My love could come home early
And find where I should be
A flour face and two eyes
Like emptied cups of tea.

My love could come and find me
Wearing an unclean room,
With an apron all around me
And my cheek rough as a crumb.

My love could come and wind me
In his new raincoat arms
And his peaked cap blind him
To my bread-and-butter charms.

If he should come home early
O the horror I should be;
But at four o'clock the horror
In his arms would be me.

I'll make my face from bottles
At seven if he comes,
Breathing scented syllables
From red lips and pink gums

While my tongue like spoons will echo
Round the china in the room
And a slim-waisted shadow
With an apron and slim limbs

[over

Like a vision float before him
And pour his cup of tea.
The horror will have vanished
But what's become of me?

Michael Baldwin

A Moment of Respect

Two things I remember about my grandfather:
his threadbare trousers, and the way he adjusted
his half-hunter watch two minutes every day.

When I asked him why he needed to know the time
   so
exactly, he said a business man could lose a fortune
by being two minutes late for an appointment.

When he died he left two meerschaum pipes
and a golden sovereign on a chain. Somebody
threw the meerschaum pipes away, and
there was an argument about the sovereign.

On the day of his burial the church clock chimed
as he was lowered down into the clay, and all
the family advanced their watches by two minutes.

Edwin Brock

Elegy for William Hubbard

Hubbard is dead, the old plumber;
who will mend our burst pipes now,
the tap that has dripped all the summer,
testing the sink's overflow?

No other like him. Young men with knowledge
of new techniques, theories from books,
may better his work straight from college,
but who will challenge his squint-eyed looks

in kitchen, bathroom, under floorboards,
rules of thumb which were often wrong;
seek as erringly stopcocks in cupboards,
or make a job last half as long?

He was a man who knew the ginnels,
alleyways, streets—the whole district;
family secrets, minor annals,
time-honoured fictions fused to fact.

Seventy years of gossip muttered
under his cap, his tufty thatch,
so that his talk was slow and clotted,
hard to follow, and too much.

As though nothing fell, none vanished,
and time were the maze of Cheetham Hill,
in which the dead with jobs unfinished
waited to hear him ring the bell.

For much he never got round to doing,
but meant to, when weather bucked up,
or worsened, or when his pipe was drawing,
or when he'd finished this cup.

I thought time, he forgot so often,
had forgotten him, but here's Death's pomp
over his house, and by the coffin
the son who will inherit his blowlamp,

tools, workshop, cart, and cornet,
(pride of Cheetham Prize Brass Band),
and there's his mourning widow, Janet,
stood at the gate he promised to mend.

Soon he will make his final journey;
shaved and silent, strangely trim,
with never a pause to talk to any-
body: how arrow-like, for him!

In St Mark's church, whose dismal tower
he pointed and painted when a lad,
they will sing his praises amidst flowers,
while, somewhere, a cellar starts to flood,

and the housewife banging his front-door
  knocker
is not surprised to find him gone,
and runs for Thwaite, who's a better worker,
and sticks at a job until it's done.

Tony Connor

Harold's Leap

Harold, are you asleep?
Harold, I remember your leap,
It may have killed you
But it was a brave thing to do.
Two promontories ran high into the sky,
He leapt from one rock to the other
And fell to the sea's smother.
Harold was always afraid to climb high,
But something urged him on,
He felt he should try.
I would not say that he was wrong,
Although he succeeded in doing
  nothing but die.
Would you?
Ever after that steep
Place was called Harold's Leap.
It was a brave thing to do.

Stevie Smith

Autobiographical Fragment

When I lived down in Devonshire
  The callers at my cottage
Were Constant Angst, the art critic,
  And old Major Courage.

Angst always brought me something nice
  To get in my good graces:
A quilt, a roll of cotton wool,
  A pair of dark glasses.

He tore up all my unpaid bills,
  Went and got my slippers,
Took the telephone off its hook
  And bolted up the shutters.

We smoked and chatted by the fire,
  Sometimes just nodding;
His charming presence made it right
  To sit and do nothing.

But then—those awful afternoons
  I walked out with the Major!
I ran up hills, down streams, through briars;
  It was sheer blue murder.

Trim in his boots, riding-breeches
  And threadbare Norfolk jacket,
He watched me, frowning, bawled commands
  To work hard and enjoy it.

[over

I asked him once why I was there,
    Except to get all dirty;
He tugged his grey moustache and snapped:
    'Young man, it's your duty.'

What duty's served by pointless, mad
    Climbing and crawling?
I tell you, I was thankful when
    The old bore stopped calling.

Kingsley Amis

Social Study

While my mother ate her heart out
And my father chewed the chairs
My sister worked in a factory
Calmly degutting pears:

The green pears like spinach
And the yellow pears like sick
She gently disembowelled
With a deft little flick.

She never seemed to worry
Or share the family fears
But thoughts like bees were buzzing
Inside her golden ears:

She jilted a tin-carpenter
And then a labeller's mate,
And finally she married
The man who nails the crate.

She had two lovely children
Called Dorothy and Clem—
They're hanging her tomorrow
For calmly degutting them.

Michael Baldwin

Nursery Rhyme of Innocence and Experience

I had a silver penny
  And an apricot tree
And I said to the sailor
  On the white quay

'Sailor O sailor
  Will you bring me
If I give you my penny
  And my apricot tree.

A fez from Algeria
  An Arab drum to beat
A little gilt sword
  And a parakeet?'

And he smiled and he kissed me
  As strong as death
And I saw his red tongue
  And I felt his sweet breath

'You may keep your penny
  And your apricot tree
And I'll bring your presents
  Back from sea.'

O the ship dipped down
  On the rim of the sky
And I waited while three
  Long summers went by

Then one steel morning
  On the white quay
I saw a grey ship
  Come in from sea

Slowly she came
  Across the bay
For her flashing rigging
  Was shot away

All round her wake
  The seabirds cried
And flew in and out
  Of the hole in her side.

Slowly she came
  In the path of the sun
And I heard the sound
  Of a distant gun

And a stranger came running
  Up to me
From the deck of the ship
  And he said, said he

'O are you the boy
  Who would wait on the quay
With the silver penny
  And the apricot tree?

[over

I've a plum-coloured fez
And a drum for thee
And a sword and a parakeet
From over the sea.'

'O where is the sailor
With bold red hair?
And what is that volley
On the bright air?

O where are the other
Girls and boys?
And why have you brought me
Children's toys?'

Charles Causley

The Slow Starter

A watched clock never moves, he said:
Leave it alone and you'll grow up.
Nor will the sulking holiday train
Start sooner if you stamp your feet.
   He left the clock to go its way;
   The whistle blew, the train went gay.

Do not press me so, she said:
Leave me alone and I will write
But not just yet, I am sure you know
The problem. Do not count the days.
   He left the calendar alone;
   The postman knocked, no letter came.

Oh never force the pace, they said;
Leave it alone, you have lots of time,
Your kind of work is none the worse
For slow maturing. Do not rush.
   He took their tip, he took his time,
   And found his time and talent gone.

Oh you have had your chance, It said;
Left it alone and it was one.
Who said a watched clock never moves?
Look at it now. Your chance was I.
   He turned and saw the accusing clock
   Race like a torrent round a rock.

Louis MacNeice

Skyman

My God I'm dead . . .
the young man said
when he saw his battered head
petalled on the crimson sand.
. . . oh Mother come and meet me now
and take my hand . . .
His body like a fountain played
along the empty esplanade
a coca-cola sign winked on
and when the moon came he was gone.

Bernard Kops

Conquerors

By sundown we came to a hidden village
Where all the air was still
And no sound met our tired ears, save
For the sorry drip of rain from blackened trees
And the melancholy song of swinging gates.
Then through a broken pane some of us saw
A dead bird in a rusting cage, still
Pressing his thin tattered breast against the bars,
His beak wide open. And
As we hurried through the weed-grown street,
A gaunt dog started up from some dark place
And shambled off on legs as thin as sticks
Into the wood, to die at least in peace.
No one had told us victory was like this;
Not one amongst us would have eaten bread
Before he'd filled the mouth of the grey child
That sprawled, stiff as a stone, before the shattered
  door.
There was not one who did not think of home.

Henry Treece

The Drawer

Their belongings were buried side by side
In a shallow bureau drawer. There was her
Crocodile handbag, letters, a brooch,
All that was in the bedside cupboard
And a small green jar she'd had for flowers.

My father's were in an envelope:
A khaki lanyard, crushed handkerchief,
Twelve cigarettes, a copying-pencil,
All he had on him when he was killed
Or all my mother wanted to keep.

I put them together, seven years ago.
Now that we've moved, my wife and I,
To a house of our own, I've taken them out.
Until we can find another spare drawer
They're packed in a cardboard box in the hall.

So this dead, middle-aged, middle-class man
Killed by a misfired shell, and his wife
Dead of cirrhosis, have left one son
Aged nine, aged nineteen, aged twenty-six,
Who has buried them both in a cardboard box.

George MacBeth

In Memory of Jane Fraser

When snow like sheep lay in the fold
And winds went begging at each door,
And the far hills were blue with cold,
And a cold shroud lay on the moor,

She kept the siege. And every day
We watched her brooding over death
Like a strong bird above its prey.
The room filled with the kettle's breath.

Damp curtains glued against the pane
Sealed time away. Her body froze
As if to freeze us all, and chain
Creation to a stunned repose.

She died before the world could stir.
In March the ice unloosed the brook
And water ruffled the sun's hair,
And a few sprinkled leaves unshook.

Geoffrey Hill

CREATURES

Robin

With a bonfire throat,
Legs of twig,
A dark brown coat,
The inspector robin
Comes where I dig.

Military man
With a bright eye
And a wooden leg,
He must scrounge and beg
Now the summer's by:

Beg at the doors,
Scrounge in the gardens,
While daylight lessens
And the grass glistens
And the ground hardens.

The toads have their vaults,
The squirrels their money,
The swifts their journey;
For him the earth's anger,
The taste of hunger.

And his unfrightened song
For the impending snows
Is also for the rose

[over

And for the great Armada
And the Phoenician trader
And the last missile raider—
It's the only one he knows.

Hal Summers

Cat

Cat, nine days old, knit out of soot,
Fragile and scrawny, squirms in the cupped palm;
Mewls, pukes, and gestures with four needy paws:
Milk; sleep; warmth; that brusque abrasive tongue
Which scours, explores the rank damp-clinging fur
Already cat, not pussy
                              —yet he learns
To live that part: house-trained, and neatly vetted,
Sleeks out to plump domestic, cuddles up,
Rolling a musky jowl on chair or shoe;
Purr modulates, and claws retract,
Till puss in jackboots serves for pantomime
And housewife's matinée.
                              But that's his guile: to mince
With delicate correctness, bland as cream,
Among the best tea-service; lapped in silk,
Conceals a yawn (eyes wincing cosily)
To watch a stooge pull strings, feed him a line,
Or mime his mousing with a ball of wool
Juggled
          —until he strikes,
Spins it off axis, sinks five searing claws
Deep into Europe, and begins
Unravelling the globe.

                              William Dunlop

Sheepdog Trials in Hyde Park
for Robert Frost

A shepherd stands at one end of the arena.
Five sheep are unpenned at the other. His dog runs
  out
In a curve to behind them, fetches them straight to
  the shepherd,
Then drives the flock round a triangular course
Through a couple of gates and back to his master;
  two
Must be sorted there from the flock, then all five
  penned.
Gathering, driving away, shedding and penning
Are the plain words for a miraculous game.

An abstract game. What can the sheepdog make of
  such
Simplified terrain?—no hills, dales, bogs, walls,
  tracks,
Only a quarter-mile plain of grass, dumb crowds
Like crowds on hoardings around it, and behind
  them
Traffic or mounds of lovers and children playing.
Well, the dog is no landscape-fancier; his whole
  concern
Is with his master's whistle, and of course
With the flock—sheep are sheep anywhere for him.

The sheep are the chanciest element. Why, for
  instance,

Go through this gate when there's on either side of
  it
No wall or hedge but huge and viable space?
Why not eat the grass instead of being pushed
  around it?
Like blobs of quicksilver on a tilting board
The flock erratically runs, dithers, breaks up,
Is reassembled: their ruling idea is the dog;
And behind the dog, though they know it not yet,
  is a shepherd.

The shepherd knows that time is of the essence
But haste calamitous. Between dog and sheep
There is always an ideal distance, a perfect angle;
But these are constantly varying, so the man
Should anticipate each move through the dog, his
  medium.
The shepherd is the brain behind the dog's brain,
But his control of dog, like dog's of sheep,
Is never absolute—that's the beauty of it.

For beautiful it is. The guided missiles,
The black-and-white angels follow each quirk and
  jink of
The evasive sheep, play grandmother's steps behind
  them,
Freeze to the ground, or leap to head off a straggler
Almost before it knows that it wants to stray,
As if radar-controlled. But they are not machines—
You can feel them feeling mastery, doubt, chagrin:
Machines don't frolic when their job is done.

[over

What's needfully done in the solitude of sheep-
    runs—
Those tough, real tasks—becomes this stylized
    game,
A demonstration of intuitive wit
Kept natural by the saving grace of error.
To lift, to fetch, to drive, to shed, to pen
Are acts I recognize, with all they mean
Of shepherding the unruly, for a kind of
Controlled woolgathering is my work too.

C. Day Lewis

Pigeons

They paddle with staccato feet
In powder-pools of sunlight,
Small blue busybodies
Strutting like fat gentlemen
With hands clasped
Under their swallowtail coats;
And, as they stump about,
Their heads like tiny hammers
Tap at imaginary nails
In non-existent walls.
Elusive ghosts of sunshine
Slither down the green gloss
Of their necks an instant, and are gone.

Summer hangs drugged from sky to earth
In limpid fathoms of silence:
Only warm dark dimples of sound
Slide like slow bubbles
From the contented throats.

Raise a casual hand—
With one quick gust
They fountain into air.

Richard Kell

View of a Pig

The pig lay on a barrow dead.
It weighed, they said, as much as three men.
Its eyes closed, pink white eyelashes.
Its trotters stuck straight out.

Such weight and thick pink bulk
Set in death seemed not just dead.
It was less than lifeless, further off.
It was like a sack of wheat.

I thumped it without feeling remorse.
One feels guilty insulting the dead,
Walking on graves. But this pig
Did not seem able to accuse.

It was too dead. Just so much
A poundage of lard and pork.
Its last dignity had entirely gone.
It was not a figure of fun.

Too dead now to pity.
To remember its life, din, stronghold
Of earthly pleasure as it had been,
Seemed a false effort, and off the point.

Too deadly factual. Its weight
Oppressed me—how could it be moved?
And the trouble of cutting it up!
The gash in its throat was shocking, but not pathetic.

Once I ran at a fair in the noise
To catch a greased piglet
That was faster and nimbler than a cat,
Its squeal was the rending of metal.

Pigs must have hot blood, they feel like ovens.
Their bite is worse than a horse's—
They chop a half-moon clean out.
They eat cinders, dead cats.

Distinctions and admirations such
As this one was long finished with.
I stared at it a long time. They were going to scald it,
Scald it and scour it like a doorstep.

Ted Hughes

Car Fights Cat

In a London crescent curving vast
A cat sat—
Between two rows of molar houses
With birdsky in each grinning gap.
Cat small—coal and snow
Road wide—a zone of tar set hard and fast
With four-wheeled speedboats cutting
A dash
      for it from
            time to time.

King Cat stalked warily midstream
As if silence were no warning on this silent road
Where even a man would certainly have crossed
With hands in pockets and been whistling.

The cat heard it, but royalty and indolence
Weighed its paws to pitboots
Held it from the dragon's-teeth of safety first and
    last,
Until some Daimler hurrying from work
Caused cat to stop and wonder where it came
    from—
Instead of zig-zag scattering to hide itself.

Maybe a deaf malevolence descended
And cat thought car would pass in front—
So spun and walked all fur and confidence
Into the dreadful tyre-treads. . . .

A wheel caught hold of it and
FEARSOME THUDS
Sounded from the night-time of black axles in
UNEQUAL FIGHT
That stopped the heart to hear it.

But cat shot out with limbs still solid,
Bolted—spitting fire and gravel
At an unjust God who built such massive
Cat-proof motorcars in His graven image,
Its mind made up to lose and therefore win
By winging towards the wisdom toothgaps of the
   canyon houses,
LEGS AND BRAIN INTACT.

Alan Sillitoe

The Lobster Pot

Who can tell how the lobster got
Into the lobster pot?
When he went in he did not doubt
There was a passage out.
There was not.

John Arden

Hedgehog

Twitching the leaves just where the drainpipe clogs
In ivy leaves and mud, a purposeful
Creature at night about its business. Dogs
Fear his stiff seriousness. He chews away

At beetles, worms, slugs, frogs. Can kill a hen
With one snap of his jaws, can taunt a snake
To death on muscled spines. Old countrymen
Tell tales of hedgehogs sucking a cow dry.

But this one, cramped by houses, fences, walls,
Must have slept here all winter in that heap
Of compost, or have inched by intervals
Through tidy gardens to this ivy bed.

And here, dim-eyed, but ears so sensitive
A voice within the house can make him freeze,
He scuffs the edge of danger; yet can live
Happily in our nights and absences.

A country creature, wary, quiet and shrewd,
He takes the milk we give him, when we're gone.
At night, our slamming voices must seem crude
To one who sits and waits for silences.

Anthony Thwaite

TWO STORIES

The History of the Flood

Bang Bang Bang
Said the nails in the Ark.

It's getting rather dark
Said the nails in the Ark.

For the rain is coming down
Said the nails in the Ark.

And you're all like to drown
Said the nails in the Ark.

Dark and black as sin,
Said the nails in the Ark.

So won't you all come in
Said the nails in the Ark.

But only two by two
Said the nails in the Ark.

So they came in two by two,
The elephant, the kangaroo,
And the gnu,
And the little tiny shrew.

Then the birds
Flocked in like winged words:

[over

Two racket-tailed motmots, two macaws,
Two nut-hatches and two
Little bright robins.

And the reptiles: the gila monster, the slow-worm,
The green mamba, the cottonmouth and the
    alligator—
All squirmed in;
And after a very lengthy walk,
Two giant Galapagos tortoises.

And the insects in their hierarchies:
A queen ant, a king ant, a queen wasp, a king wasp,
A queen bee, a king bee,
And all the beetles, bugs, and mosquitoes,
Cascaded in like glittering, murmurous jewels.

But the fish had their wish;
For the rain came down.
People began to drown:
The wicked, the rich—
They gasped out bubbles of pure gold,
Which exhalations
Rose to the constellations.

So for forty days and forty nights
They were on the waste of waters
In those cramped quarters.
It was very dark, damp and lonely.
There was nothing to see, but only
The rain which continued to drop.
It did not stop.

So Noah sent forth a Raven. The Raven said
    'Kark!
I will not go back to the Ark.'
The Raven was footloose,
He fed on the bodies of the rich—
Rich with vitamins and goo.
They had become bloated,
And everywhere they floated.
The Raven's heart was black,
He did not come back.
It was not a nice thing to do:
Which is why the Raven is a token of wrath,
And creaks like a rusty gate
When he crosses your path; and Fate
Will grant you no luck that day:
The Raven is fey:
You were meant to have a scare.
Fortunately in England
The Raven is rather rare.

Then Noah sent forth a Dove
She did not want to rove.
She longed for her love—
The other turtle dove—
(For her no other dove)!
She brought back a twig from an olive-tree.
There is no more beautiful tree
Anywhere on the earth,
Even when it comes to birth
From six weeks under the sea.

[over

She did not want to rove.
She wanted to take her rest,
And to build herself a nest
All in the olive grove
She wanted to make love.
She thought that was the best.

The Dove was not a rover;
So they knew that the rain was over.
Noah and his wife got out
(They had become rather stout)
And Japhet, Ham, and Shem.
(The same could be said of them.)
They looked up at the sky.
The earth was becoming dry.

Then the animals came ashore—
There were more of them than before:
There were two dogs and a litter of puppies;
There were a tom-cat and two tib-cats
And two litters of kittens—cats
Do not obey regulations;
And, as you might expect,
A quantity of rabbits.

God put a rainbow in the sky.
They wondered what it was for.
There had never been a rainbow before.
The rainbow was a sign;
It looked like a neon sign—

Seven colours arched in the skys:
What should it publicize?
They looked up with wondering eyes.

It advertises Mercy
Said the nails in the Ark.

Mercy Mercy Mercy
Said the nails in the Ark.

Our God is merciful
Said the nails in the Ark.

Merciful and gracious
Bang Bang Bang Bang.

John Heath-Stubbs

First Fight

Tonight, then, is the night;
Stretched on the massage table,
Wrapped in his robe, he breathes
Liniment and sweat
And tries to close his ears
To the roaring of the crowd,
A mirky sea of noise
That bears upon its tide
The frail sound of the bell
And brings the cunning fear
That he might not do well,
Not fear of bodily pain
But that his tight-lipped pride
Might be sent crashing down,
His white ambition slain,
Knocked spinning the glittering crown.
How could his spirit bear
That ignominious fall?
Not hero but a clown
Spurned or scorned by all.
The thought appals, and he
Feels sudden envy for
The roaring crowd outside
And wishes he were there
Anonymous and safe,
Calm in the tolerant air,

Would almost choose to be
Anywhere but here.

II

The door blares open suddenly,
The room is sluiced with row;
His second says, 'We're on next fight,
We'd better get going now.
You got your gumshield, haven't you?
Just loosen up—that's right—
Don't worry, Boy, you'll be okay
Once you start to fight.'

Out of the dressing-room, along,
The neutral passage to
The yelling cavern where the ring
Through the haze of blue
Tobacco smoke is whitewashed by
The aching glare of light:
Geometric ropes are stretched as taut
As this boy's nerves are tight.

And now he's in his corner where
He tries to look at ease;
He feels the crowd's sharp eyes as they
Prick and pry and tease;
He hears them murmur like the sea
Or some great dynamo:
They are not hostile yet they wish
To see his lifeblood flow.

[over

His adversary enters now;
The Boy risks one quick glance;
He does not see an enemy
But something there by chance,
Not human even, but a cold
Abstraction to defeat,
A problem to be solved by guile,
Quick hands and knowing feet.
The fighters' names are shouted out;
They leave their corners for
The touch of gloves and brief commands;
The disciplines of war.
Back in their corners, stripped of robes,
They hear the bell clang *one*
Brazen syllable which says
The battle has begun.

III

Bite on gumshield,
Guard held high,
The crowd are silenced,
All sounds die.
Lead with the left,
Again, again;
Watch for the opening,
Feint and then
Hook to the body
But he's blocked it and
Slammed you back
With a fierce right hand.

Hang on grimly,
The fog will clear,
Sweat in your nostrils,
Grease and fear.
You're hurt and staggering,
Shocked to know
That the story's altered:
He's the hero!

But the mist is clearing,
The referee snaps
A rapid warning
And he smartly taps
Your hugging elbow
And then you step back
Ready to counter
The next attack,
But the first round finishes
Without mishap.
You suck in the air
From the towel's skilled flap.
A voice speaks urgently
Close to your ear:
'Keep your left going, Boy,
Stop him getting near.
He wants to get close to you,
So jab him off hard;
When he tries to slip below,
Never mind your guard,
Crack him with a solid right,
Hit him on the chin,

[over

A couple downstairs
And then he'll pack it in.'

Slip in the gumshield
Bite on it hard,
Keep him off with your left,
Never drop your guard.
Try a left hook,
But he crosses with a right
Smack on your jaw
And Guy Fawkes' Night
Flashes and dazzles
Inside your skull,
Your knees go bandy
And you almost fall.
Keep the left jabbing,
Move around the ring,
Don't let him catch you with
Another hook or swing.
Keep your left working,
Keep it up high,
Stab it out straight and hard,
Again—above the eye.
Sweat in the nostrils,
But nothing now of fear,
You're moving smooth and confident
In comfortable gear.
Jab with the left again,
Quickly move away;
Feint and stab another in,
See him duck and sway.

Now for the pay-off punch,
Smash it hard inside;
It thuds against his jaw, he falls,
Limbs spread wide.
And suddenly you hear the roar,
Hoarse music of the crowd,
Voicing your hot ecstasy,
Triumphant, male and proud.

IV

Now, in the sleepless darkness of his room
The Boy, in bed, remembers. Suddenly
The victory tastes sour. The man he fought
Was not a thing, as lifeless as a broom,
He was a man who hoped and trembled too;
What of him now? What was *he* going through?
And then the Boy bites hard on resolution:
Fighters can't pack pity with their gear,
And yet a bitter taste stays with the notion;
He's forced to swallow down one treacherous tear.
But that's the last. He is a boy no longer;
He is a man, a fighter, such as jeer
At those who make salt beads with melting eyes,
Whatever might cry out, is hurt, or dies.

                              Vernon Scannell

SCENES

Coming to England

My father moved house the day I was born
(Mother must've been swift as a kangaroo)
Like a bird that has gathered stalks of corn
For its nest and found it's time to migrate.
I arrived early and father was late
And mother was busy as a sparrow.

Two years passed and I hadn't said a word
When cart-wheels creaked outside the door.
Out came the beds, the pots and pans, and, Lord!
We were moving house again. We ran out,
In seven years, of houses in Sialkot.
Now it was autumn, the rains had stopped, so

We did the next best thing and followed the birds
A thousand miles south to Bombay. The sea
Was warm, the hills were green, and our cupboards
Were full of meat and milk. So, shrewd as a mouse,
Father bought land and planned to build a house.
Four acres it was with a mango-tree.

The world war ended, the price of land rose,
But down went father's *Import & Export*,
And down went, too, 'The Plans of Mr Ghose'.
The sea was blue, the horizons were pale,
Father stroked his paunch that bulged like a whale's.
Trains end in Bombay, Bombay is a port:

[over

We thought of Brazil, we thought of Uganda,
But England, O England, it had to be.
Mother dragged me along as a child her panda,
We took the next ship to Tilbury Docks.
It was spring in London, I saw flocks
Of birds alight upon tree after tree.

Zulfikar Ghose

Disturbances

After the darkness has come
And the distant planes catch fire
In the dusk, coming home,
And the tall church spire
No longer stands on the hill
And the streets are quiet except
For a car-door slamming—well,
You might say the houses slept.
An owl calls from a tree.

This is my house and home,
A place where for several years
I've settled, to which I've come
Happily, set my shears
To the hedge which fronts the place,
Had decorators in,
Altered a former face
To a shape I can call my own.
An owl calls from a tree.

Only, sometimes at night
Or running downhill for a train,
I suddenly catch sight
Of a world not named and plain
And without hedges or walls:
A jungle of noises, fears,
No lucid intervals,
No calm exteriors.
An owl calls from a tree.

[over

The place I live in has
A name on the map, a date
For all that is or was.
I avoid hunger and hate:
I have a bed for the night:
The dishes are stacked in the rack:
I remember to switch off the light:
I turn and lie on my back.
An owl calls from a tree.

Anthony Thwaite

Street Scene

Housewives stand at their doorsteps,
Stout arms folded across their breasts,
Saying yes about the weather
And poor Hugh Porter who died last week—
It's going to rain, God rest his soul,
He never looked after hisself.

Three young children, shouting their games,
Pause to watch the mourners pass,
Unused to so much black in the summer
And so many old women looking so clean.
Rain, and the street is grey with drizzle
As the coffin is bumped through the door.

Four shiny black limousines,
Too big by far for Minden Street,
Move off slowly through the rain
Behind the hearse fit for a queen
That carries Old Hugh, rich in his wreaths,
To lie with his wife again.

Shaking their heads, the housewives
Go in to make the tea;
The children play in the puddles
And shout their games again.
And, on turning the corner of Minden Street,
Hugh Porter's hearse splashes a young girl's feet.

Jack Marriott

The 'Black' Country

'But it is not Black,' they will tell you, 'any longer,
    not really Black.'
And of course they have the right ideas, and are
    right.
Progress is always changing colour: blushes more
    deeply or now scowls darkly, or turns pale.

True, how can it be called Black?—with its shining
    cubes of metallic branch-groceries,
And the tin gleam of the fish saloon, tiled like a
    public lavatory.
Where the fried fish floats, in Sargasso seas of chips.

It is not Black, in the sense that the desert is Red
With a history of running sores, or that the grass
    was Green.
Not black, as Babylon was Scarlet, or the Blood,
As violets are Violet, as Pythagoras' thigh was
    Golden, or corn is—
Not Black as the satin back of this black horse is
    Black.

So we shall call it the Grey Country, out of
    deference.
But Grey is slyer than Black: 'Why, I am practically
    White.'

                                          D. J. Enright

A Child is Singing

A child singing
And nobody listening
But the child who is singing:

Bulldozers grab the earth and shower it.
The house is on fire.
Gardeners wet the earth and flower it.
The house is on fire,
The houses are on fire.
Fetch the fire engine, the fire engine's on fire.
We will have to hide in a hole.
We will burn slow like coal.
All the people are on fire

And a child is singing
And nobody listening
But the child who is singing.

Adrian Mitchell

Landscape as Werewolf

Near here, the last grey wolf
In England was clubbed down. Still,
After two hundred years, the same pinched wind
Rakes through his cairn of bones

As he squats quiet, watching daylight seep
Away from the scarred granite, and its going drain
The hills' bare faces. Far below,
A tiny bus twists on its stringy path
And scuttles home around a darkening bend.

The fells contract, regroup in starker forms;
Dusk tightens on them, as the wind gets up
And stretches hungrily: tensed at the nape,
The coarse heath bristles like a living pelt.

The sheep are all penned in. Down at the pub
They sing, and shuttle darts: the hostellers
Dubbin their heavy boots. Above the crags
The first stars prick their eyes and bide their time.

William Dunlop

Tenby

In winter wound in a cocoon of warm
walls, dug discreetly in, snug as a butler
in a pantry, the essential form

of the place remains but all else sleeps;
even the little waves arch neatly on
the sunlit shore with prim and poodle leaps.

Summer romps in on charabanc and train:
sad men in paper caps consume ice cream
or candy floss while sheltering from the rain,

and seagulls rest their red, plebeian feet
upon Prince Albert's alabaster head.
But O the joy of Welsh upon the street!

Raymond Garlick

Sunday Morning in the North

Because of sunlight the young girls collect
Where two rows of dull houses intersect,
To sum up boys, and laugh, and understand.
Old men sit long and dream of plots of land.
Women, like ships busy with their small freight,
Now lean at doorways where the dinners wait
No less mysteriously contained than I
Within those pockets poems like dark birds fly.

Michell Raper

Holiday

When the boys came out of school they threw up
  their caps,
And the air was striped with their spinning.

When the girls came out of school they pulled off
  their stockings,
And the roof-tops streamed with long black banners.

When the boys and girls came out of school
All the bells of the town choked with their chiming.

When the boys walked in the streets their shoes
  purred on the asphalt,
And the corners were bright as butterflies.

When the girls walked in the streets their legs shone
  in shop-windows,
And the cinema-queues trembled with love.

When the boys and girls walked in the streets
It was like a cathedral decked with worshippers.

And when the boys and girls went back to school
All the clocks of the town wrung their rusted hands.

Julian Mitchell

In Midwinter a Wood was . . .

In midwinter a wood was
where the sand-coloured deer ran
through quietness.
It was a marvellous thing
to see those deer running.

Softer than ashes
snow lay all winter where they ran,
and in the wood a holly tree was.
God, it was a marvellous thing
to see the deer running.

Between lime trunks grey or green
branch-headed stags went by
silently trotting.
A holly tree dark and crimson
sprouted at the wood's centre, thick and high
without a whisper, no other berry so fine.

Outside the wood was black midwinter,
over the downs that reared so solemn
wind rushed in gales, and strong here
wrapped around wood and holly fire
(where deer among the close limes ran)
with a storming circle of its thunder.
Under the trees it was a marvellous thing
to see the deer running.

Peter Levi

The Poster

Why do they pose
(This man and girl)
Oblivious
To the traffic's whirl
At the street corner
Where the clinging dark
Illumined by the neon lamp
And the sky sign's spark?

Why do they hold
Communion each to each
Oblivious
To the blurred and crowded speech
Of a city's rhythm
Flowing by—
Vehicle and human tone,
And the street-vendor's cry?

Why do their eyes,
Now blurred by rain
Show neither joy
Or suffer pain?
In their love-fast
Silence, in city's boom,
A neon-lighted kiss
Is knit with doom!

[over

Not to the crowded street—
The transient kiss—
Is love apparent
In their brief bliss.
Brief—for the moments tell
Their love shall stay
There till the wind and the endless rain
Wash it away!

Rex Taylor

Autobiographical Note

Beeston, the place, near Nottingham;
We lived there for three years or so.
Each Saturday at two o'clock
We queued up for the matinée,
All the kids for streets around
With snotty noses, giant caps,
Cut down coats and heavy boots,
The natural enemies of cops
And schoolteachers. Profane and hoarse
We scrambled, yelled and fought until
The Picture Palace opened up
And then, like Hamelin children, forced
Our bony way into the Hall.
That much is easy to recall;
Also the reek of chewing-gum,
Gob-stoppers and liquorice,
But of the flickering myths themselves
Not much remains. The hero was
A milky, wide-brimmed hat, a shape
Astride the arched white stallion.
The villain's horse and hat were black.
Disbelief did not exist
And laundered virtue always won
With quicker gun and harder fist
And all of us applauded it.
Yet I remember moments when
In solitude I'd find myself
Brooding on the sooty man,

[over

The bristling villain, who could move
Imagination in a way
The well-shaved hero never could,
And even warm the nervous heart
With something oddly close to love.

Vernon Scannell

Abersoch

There was that headland, asleep on the sea,
The air full of thunder and the far air
Brittle with lightning; there was that girl
Riding her cycle, hair at half-mast;
And the men smoking, the dinghies at rest
On the calm tide. There were people going
About their business, while the storm grew
Louder and nearer and did not break.

Why do I remember these few things,
That were rumours of life, not life itself
That was being lived fiercely, where the storm
  raged?
Was it just that the girl smiled,
Though not at me, and the men smoking
Had the look of those who have come safely home?

R. S. Thomas

The Fox-coloured Pheasant Enjoyed His Peace . . .

The fox-coloured pheasant enjoyed his peace,
there were no labourers in the wheat,
dogs were stretched out at ease,
the empty road echoed my feet.

It was the time for owls' voices,
trees were dripping dark like rain,
and sheep made night-time noises
as I went down the hill lane.

In the streets of the still town
I met a man in the lamplight,
he stood in the alley that led down
to the harbour and the sea out of sight.

Who do you want? he asked me,
Who are you looking for in this place?
The houses echoed us emptily
and the lamp shone on his face.

Does your girl live here?
(There were no girls or sailors about.)
I have no girl anywhere,
I want a ship putting out.

He stood under the lamplight
and I stepped up close to him,
his eyes burned like fires at night
and the lamp seemed dim.

He came closer up and pressed
his crooked knee to my knee,
and his chest to my chest,
and held my shoulders and wrestled with me.

It was the middle time of night
with five hours to run till day,
but the sky was crimson and bright
before he stood out of my way.

I ran past as quick as I could
and the wet stones rang loudly
along the wharf where the ships stood
and the sea lifting proudly.

Peter Levi

At Any Rate

'He's dead!' they shouted as he left his motor-bike
And catapulted twenty feet through air
And dented earth. They wanted him to be dead
Out of a sort of innocent malignance
And being born dramatists the lot of them.
And dead he was in the end. The blood gushed
From his ears. 'He's dead,' they told the doctor,
Though he wasn't, as the doctor saw at once,
By any means dead. 'Officer,' they said, 'he's dead.
He ought to be at any rate if he's human.'
And in the end they were right, dead right.
An hour later, by the tangled bike
(Considered by the crowd by no means done for)
They were still standing, very much alive—
As they ought to be, at any rate if they're human.

James Michie

Leaving Town

It was impossible to leave the town.
Bumping across a maze of obsolete rails
Three times we reached the gasworks and reversed.
We could not get away from the canal;
Dead cats, dead hopes, in those grey deeps im-
    mersed,
Over our efforts breathed a spectral prayer.
The cattle-market and the gospel-hall
Returned like fictions of our own despair,
And like Hesperides the suburbs seemed,
Shining far off towards the guiltless fields.
We finished in a little cul-de-sac
Where on the pavement sat a ragged girl
Mourning beside a jug-and-bottle entrance.
Once more we turned the car and started back.

James Reeves

The Day Larry was Stretched

The dawn they did Larry the speckled dust
lifted a twisted curtain round
the whistler corner and creased papers
danced to the chill of a street wind.

Over the gutters the leching sparrows
pick-axed an hour grey as a hat
with early caring, and blue pigeons
clattered soft drums on the monument.

A yellow of lemons and child's ribbons
stroked a slate skyline; upon its wall
willow herb whipped a flicker of stem
to a storm of seed through a blitzed school.

A door slammed hollow, and glass clangours
of blue steel crates down the mild-washed street
turned over the sleepers. A mild policeman
flicked at the dust on his mirror boots.

At the island of farm in a sea of suburb
the cock stretched its neck in a raw scream
friendly as traffic. The empty station
blew papers after the first train.

The dawn they did Larry the rain scattered
pocks on the river, specks of lead
stinging the smooth, and an old jacket
drifted downtide like a drowned god.

Robin Skelton

I Remember, I Remember

Coming up England by a different line
For once, early in the cold new year,
We stopped, and, watching men with number-
    plates
Sprint down the platform to familiar gates,
'Why, Coventry!' I exclaimed. 'I was born here.'

I leant far out, and squinnied for a sign
That this was still the town that had been 'mine'
So long, but found I wasn't even clear
Which side was which. From where those cycle-
    crates
Were standing, had we annually departed

For all those family hols? . . . A whistle went:
Things moved. I sat back, staring at my boots.
'Was that,' my friend smiled, 'where you "have your
    roots"?'
No, only where my childhood was unspent,
I wanted to retort, just where I started:

By now I've got the whole place clearly charted.
Our garden, first: where I did not invent
Blinding theologies of flowers and fruits,
And wasn't spoken to by an old hat.
And here we have that splendid family

[over

I never ran to when I got depressed,
The boys all biceps and the girls all chest,
Their comic Ford, their farm where I could be
'Really myself.' I'll show you, come to that,
The bracken where I never trembling sat,

Determined to go through with it; where she
Lay back, and 'all became a burning mist'.
And in those offices, my doggerel
Was not set up in blunt ten-point, nor read
By a distinguished cousin of the mayor,

Who didn't call and tell my father *There*
Before us, had we the gift to see ahead—
'You look as if you wished the place in Hell,'
My friend said, 'judging from your face.' 'Oh well,
I suppose it's not the place's fault,' I said.

'Nothing, like something, happens anywhere.'
                                        Philip Larkin

POINTS OF VIEW

Rising Five

'I'm rising five,' he said,
'Not four,' and little coils of hair
Unclicked themselves upon his head.
His spectacles, brimful of eyes to stare
At me and the meadow, reflected cones of light
Above his toffee-buckled cheeks. He'd been alive
Fifty-six months or perhaps a week more:

                                        not four,
But rising five.

Around him in the field the cells of spring
Bubbled and doubled; buds unbuttoned; shoot
And stem shook out the creases from their frills,
And every tree was swilled with green.
It was the season after blossoming,
Before the forming of the fruit:

                        not May,
But rising June.

                        And in the sky
The dust dissected the tangential light:
                        not day,
But rising night;
                not now,
But rising soon.

The new buds push the old leaves from the bough.
We drop our youth behind us like a boy
Throwing away his toffee wrappers. We never see
   the flower,

                                        [over

103

But only the fruit in the flower; never the fruit,
But only the rot in the fruit. We look for the mar-
    riage bed
In the baby's cradle, we look for the grave in the bed:
                                not living,
But rising dead.

Norman Nicholson

The Secret Sharer

Over the ankles in snow and numb past pain
I stared up at my window three stories high:
From a white street unconcerned as a dead eye,
I patiently called my name again and again.

The curtains were lit, through glass were lit by
    doubt.
And there was I, within the room alone.
In the empty wind I stood and shouted on:
But O what if the strange head should peer out?

Suspended taut between two equal fears
I was like to be torn apart by their strong pull:
What, I asked, if I never hear my call?
And what if it reaches my insensitive ears?

Fixed in my socket of thought I saw them move
Aside, I saw that some uncertain hand
Had touched the curtains. Mine, I wondered? And,
At this instant, the wind turned in its groove.

The wind turns in its groove and I am here
Lying in bed, the snow and street outside;
Fire-glow still reassuring; dark defied.
The wind turns in its groove: I am still there.

Thom Gunn

Peach, Plum, or Apricot

Peach, Plum, or Apricot!
How much money have you got?
If you've got a bob or two,
I will bring some home for you.

Apricot, Peach, or Plum!
We may get blown to kingdom come,
Let us eat our fruit before
Our parents go again to war.

Plum, Apricot, or Peach!
Hide the stone from out their reach,
So that it falls into the earth
And brings another world to birth.

Bernard Kops

Dooley is a Traitor

'So then you won't fight?'
'Yes, your Honour,' I said, 'that's right.'
'Now is it that you simply aren't willing,
Or have you a fundamental moral objection to killing?'
Says the judge, blowing his nose
And making his words stand to attention in long rows.
I stand to attention too, but with half a grin
(In my time I've done a good many in).
'No objection at all, sir,' I said.
'There's a deal of the world I'd rather see dead—
Such as Johnny Stubbs or Fred Settle or my last
    landlord, Mr Syme.
Give me a gun and your blessing, your Honour,
    and I'll be killing them all the time.
But my conscience says a clear no
To killing a crowd of gentlemen I don't know.
Why, I'd as soon think of killing a worshipful judge,
High-court, like yourself (against whom, God
    knows, I've got no grudge—
So far), as murder a heap of foreign folk.
If you've got no grudge, you've got no joke
To laugh at after.'
                        Now the words never come flowing
Proper for me till I get the old pipe going.
And just as I was poking
Down baccy, the judge looks up sharp with 'No smoking,
Mr Dooley. We're not fighting this war for fun.
And we want a clearer reason why you refuse to
    carry a gun.

[over

This war is not a personal feud, it's a fight
Against wrong ideas on behalf of the Right.
Mr Dooley, won't you help to destroy evil ideas?'
'Ah, your Honour, here's
The tragedy,' I said. 'I'm not a man of the mind.
I couldn't find it in my heart to be unkind
To an idea. I wouldn't know one if I saw one. I
    haven't one of my own.
So I'd best be leaving other people's alone.'
'Indeed,' he sneers at me, 'this defence is
Curious for someone with convictions in two senses.
A criminal invokes conscience to his aid
To support an individual withdrawal from a com-
    munal crusade
Sanctioned by God, led by the Church, against a
    godless, churchless nation!'
I asked his Honour for a translation.
'You talk of conscience,' he said. 'What do you know
    of the Christian Creed?'
'Nothing, sir, except what I can read.
That's the most you can hope for from us jail-birds.
I just open the book here and there and look at the
    words.
And I find when the Lord himself misliked an evil notion
He turned it into a pig and drove it squealing over a
    cliff into the ocean,
And the loony ran away
And lived to think another day.
There was a clean job done and no blood shed!
Everybody happy and forty wicked thoughts
    drowned dead.

A neat and Christian murder. None of your mad
    slaughter
Throwing away the brains with the blood and the
    baby with the bathwater.
Now I look at the war as a sportsman. It's a matter
    of choosing
The decentest way of losing.
Heads or tails, losers or winners,
We all lose, we're all damned sinners.
And I'd rather be with the poor cold people at the
    wall that's shot
Than the bloody guilty devils in the firing-line, in
    Hell and keeping hot.'
'But what right, Dooley, what right,' he cried,
'Have you to say the Lord is on your side?'
'That's a dirty crooked question,' back I roared.
'I said not the Lord was on my side, but I was on the
    side of the Lord.'
Then he was up at me and shouting,
But by and by he calms: 'Now we're not doubting
Your sincerity, Dooley, only your arguments,
Which don't make sense.'
('Hullo,' I thought, 'that's the wrong way round.
I may be skylarking a bit, but my brainpan's sound.')
Then biting his nail and sugaring his words sweet:
'Keep your head, Mr Dooley. Religion is clearly not
    up your street.
But let me ask you as a plain patriotic fellow
Whether you'd stand there so smug and yellow
If the foe were attacking your own dear sister.'
'I'd knock their brains out, mister,

[over

On the floor,' I said. 'There,' he says kindly, 'I knew
you were no pacifist.
It's your straight duty as a man to enlist.
The enemy is at the door.' You could have downed
Me with a feather. 'Where?' I gasp, looking round.
'Not this door,' he says angered. 'Don't play the clown.
But they're two thousand miles away planning to
do us down.
Why, the news is full of the deeds of those murders
and rapers.'
'Your Eminence,' I said, 'my father told me never to
believe the papers
But to go by my eyes,
And at two thousand miles the poor things can't
tell truth from lies.'
His fearful spectacles glittered like the moon: 'For
the last time what right
Has a man like you to refuse to fight?'
'More right,' I said, 'than you.
You've never murdered a man, so you don't know
what it is I won't do.
I've done it in good hot blood, so haven't I the right
to make bold
To declare that I shan't do it in cold?'
Then the judge rises in a great rage
And writes *Dooley is a Traitor* in black upon a page
And tells me I must die.
'What, me?' says I.
'If you still won't fight.'
'Well, yes, your Honour,' I said, 'that's right.'

James Michie

Lament for the Cowboy Life

Where the trails met, our herds met, too,
And mingled on their lowing way to slaughter.
Spying ahead, the sky a parching blue,
We tortured valleys for their news of water.

And water found, we shared our food.
And settling by one fire watched nights together.
Waking each day to coffee freshly brewed
I never hungered for more gentle weather.

When outlaws ambushed us, we blazed them back,
We flushed them out, like partridges, from cover.
A double grave means someone's grief and lack,
But who they were the desert can discover.

Coming at last down to the railhead
We sorted herds and haggled for fair prices.
The hands reported not one beast was dead,
Their massive flanks shipped off for butchers' slices.

And you had business there, and mine was on,
Three thousand miles across this continent.
And so we parted, partners, business done,
And whiskey pledged our friendship permanent.

From Salem to Salinas grows this land,
And Massachusetts grass grows dollar-green.
And yet I wish I'd stayed a cattle-hand
And never knew a country lies between.

[over

Against my office-window bumps the sun.
Now God herds us, as we those cattle then.
But every evening, on the homeward run,
I ride with cowboys, not with subway men.

Julian Mitchell

The Citizens

After the marsh was drained and its vast monsters
Had gasped their lives out in the well-rinsed air,
Our city corporation cleaned the fosse up
And charged us sixpence to see Grendell's lair.
We thought that with the Great Panjandrum
   banished
An era of sweet dreams was sure to start;
But gracious no, only his cave has vanished;
Don't look now, but he's walking in your heart.

After Sir Hercules had combed the mountains
And killed the Nemean lion, our woods were bare.
On feast days now we can go out to picnic
And if it rains take shelter in its lair;
The pebbles and the moss are quite enchanting.
I think I hear the ancient roaring start.
What's that you say? I said the ancient roaring,
Excuse me but it's coming from your heart.

Upon our museum shelves we keep the omens
That after school before they go to bed
Children may see some curious time-worn bauble,
A pickled toad, a stone, a Gorgon's head.
Why do they cry in sleep, the silly children,
Of birds that speak, of snakes that hiss and dart
Upon a woman's scalp? Put them to silence.
You cannot stop the language of the heart.

[over

In days gone by the warriors would sit feasting,
Then freeze to silence at the slow footfall
Of Grendell's furious dam who rocked the postern,
Then strode through snapping beams into the hall.
That monster comes no more by field or river,
But still our dwelling-place is torn apart
By human hands—like mine—our children
     ravaged;
Oh, hide me from the fury of the heart.

Thomas Blackburn

The Hunt

Out of the old cold dark nothing but nothing and
    death.
The hunter stands, stares through the smoke of his
    breath.
A merest movement wrinkles the horizon and the
    man's stare
Freezes; the smoke thins to a pulse-beat stirring the
    air.
The man merges into his shadow, moves as the wind
    does,
Insistently, quickly. On and in, quiet as breath, he
    goes
Till death's cry stains the air, spreading out and out
Into the silence that curves and eddies all about.
The hunter comes heavily home, quick breath
    pluming.
When next he hunts his step will have still less
    spring.

Richard Weber

Death on a Live Wire

Treading a field I saw afar
A laughing fellow climbing the cage
That held the grinning tensions of wire,
Alone, and no girl gave him courage.

Up he climbed on the diamond struts,
Diamond cut diamond, till he stood
With the insulators brooding like owls
And all their live wisdom, if he would.

I called to him climbing and asked him to say
What thrust him into the singeing sky:
The one word he told me the wind took away,
So I shouted again, but the wind passed me by

And the gust of his answer tore at his coat
And stuck him stark on the lightning's bough;
Humanity screeched in his manacled throat
And he cracked with flame like a figure of straw.

Turning, burning, he dangled black,
A hot sun swallowing at his fork
And shaking embers out of his back,
Planting his shadow of fear in the chalk.

O then he danced an incredible dance
With soot in his sockets, hanging at heels;
Uprooted mandrakes screamed in his loins,
His legs thrashed and lashed like electric eels;

For now he embraced the talent of iron,
The white-hot ore that comes from the hill,
The Word out of which the electrons run,
The snake in the rod and the miracle;

And as he embraced it the girders turned black,
Fused metal wept and great tears ran down,
Till his fingers like snails at last came unstuck
And he fell through the cage of the sun.

Michael Baldwin

Street Gang

Everywhere they are waiting. In silence.
In boredom. Staring into space.
Reflecting on nothing, or on violence
That is long since past. Wondering.
Wondering what will happen next.
Whatever it is is beyond their control
Or understanding. They are waiting. Not vexed
By any thoughts of the uncertain future
(Apparently); absorbed in the present
Shot through with spasms of the violent
Past. They are waiting. . . .
                              Coffe-cups
Battle. Matches flare. Cigarettes
Glow in the darkness of the milk-bar
Or the drug-store. Hour after hour
They sit, indistinguishable
In the darkness: oblivious of who they are
Or what they want: except to be together.

Then suddenly it happens. A motor-cycle
Explodes outside, a cup smashes,
They are on their feet, identified
At last as living creatures.
The universal silence is shattered,
The law overthrown, chaos
Has come again . . .
                        The victim has been kicked,
Gouged, stamped on, crucified.

His blood streams across the pavement.
And none of them knows why.
Tomorrow their endless vigil
Will begin again. Perhaps nothing will happen.
Or perhaps, this time, a single
Scapegoat will not suffice. . . .

H. Webster

Your Attention Please

YOUR ATTENTION PLEASE—
The Polar DEW has just warned that
A nuclear rocket strike of
At least one thousand megatons
Has been launched by the enemy
Directly at our major cities.
This announcement will take
Two and a quarter minutes to make,
You therefore have a further
Eight and a quarter minutes
To comply with the shelter
Requirements published in the Civil
Defence Code—section Atomic Attack.
A specially shortened Mass
Will be broadcast at the end
Of this announcement—
Protestant and Jewish services
Will begin simultaneously—
Select your wavelength immediately
According to instructions
In the Defence Code. Do not
Take well-loved pets (including birds)
Into your shelter—they will consume
Fresh air. Leave the old and bed-
Ridden, you can do nothing for them.
Remember to press the sealing
Switch when everyone is in
The shelter. Set the radiation
Aerial, turn on the geiger barometer.
Turn off your Television now.
Turn off your radio immediately

The services end. At the same time
Secure explosion plugs in the ears
Of each member of your family. Take
Down your plasma flasks. Give your children
The pills marked one and two
In the C.D. green container, then put
Them to bed. Do not break
The inside airlock seals until
The radiation All Clear shows
(Watch for the cuckoo in your
Perspex panel), or your District
Touring Doctor rings your bell.
If before this your air becomes
Exhausted or if any of your family
Is critically injured, administer
The capsules marked 'Valley Forge'
(Red pocket in No. 1 Survival Kit)
For painless death. (Catholics
Will have been instructed by their priests
What to do in this eventuality.)
This announcement is ending. Our President
Has already given orders for
Massive retaliation—it will be
Decisive. Some of us may die.
Remember, statistically
It is not likely to be you.
All flags are flying fully dressed
On Government buildings—the sun is shining.
Death is the least we have to fear.
We are all in the hands of God,
Whatever happens happens by His will.
Now go quickly to your shelters.

Peter Porter

And Because

'A star shines in the sky. He follows you. When you move he moves.'—
Dictionary made by six-year-olds.

and because we listened

and listened not only among the incense and
chanting
not only at premises of licensed amusement
not only in dreams or to the wisdom of actuaries

but listened also to the wind when we were lost in
the mountains
listened in Petticoat Lane
or listened to silence and a heartbeat after the dawn

a word was spoken

and because we looked

and looked not only among the tinsel and holly
not only at neon bottles for Magog
not only at paper lanterns and the full moon

but looked over the sea to the west at sunset
looked also at the Auroral ballet
or looked at a glow-worm and the light of word

a star shone in the sky

and because we walked
and walked not only along paved cloisters
not only to the holy cities of seven religions
not only by fieldpaths or Fleet Street

but walked also from Tolpuddle Hiroshima Sophia-
   town
walked awake and sleeping
or walked the King's Road as far as the Word's
   Beginning

the star came with us

and because the hotel was booked up for Christmas
we were boarded out with a girl who was nursing
   her baby

and the star stopped with us

and next day we continued our journey

John Knight

Au Jardin des Plantes

The gorilla lay on his back,
One hand cupped under his head,
Like a man.

Like a labouring man tired with work,
A strong man with his strength burnt away
In the toil of earning a living.

Only of course he was not tired out with work,
Merely with boredom; his terrible strength
All burnt away by prodigal idleness.

A thousand days, and then a thousand days,
Idleness licked away his beautiful strength
He having no need to earn a living.

It was all laid on, free of charge.
We maintained him, not for doing anything,
But for being what he was.

And so that Sunday morning he lay on his back,
Like a man, like a worn-out man,
One hand cupped under his terrible hard head.

Like a man, like a man,
One of those we maintain, not for doing anything,
But for being what they are.

A thousand days, and then a thousand days,
With everything laid on, free of charge,
They cup their heads in prodigal idleness.

John Wain

Index of First Lines

Index of Poets